Ingenious
Puzzles
for Word Lovers

GEORGE BREDEHORN

Official
American Mensa
Puzzle Book

Sterling Publishing Co., Inc.
New York

Edited and designed by Peter Gordon

10 9 8 7 6 5 4 3 2 1

Published by Sterling Publishing Company, Inc.
387 Park Avenue South, New York, N.Y. 10016
© 2000 by George Bredehorn
Distributed in Canada by Sterling Publishing
c/o Canadian Manda Group, One Atlantic Avenue, Suite 105
Toronto, Ontario, Canada M6K 3E7
Distributed in Great Britain and Europe by Cassell PLC
Wellington House, 125 Strand, London WC2R 0BB, England
Distributed in Australia by Capricorn Link (Australia) Pty Ltd.
P.O. Box 6651, Baulkham Hills, Business Centre, NSW 2153, Australia

Sterling ISBN 0-8069-3540-5

CONTENTS

INTRODUCTION

I'm not a typical word game lover. I love words, but I don't enjoy solving crosswords. To me, crosswords are "impure." You need to know obscure words and useless trivia to solve them. The puzzles in this book are different. They require no trivial knowledge, and virtually every word in all the puzzles can be found in a good college-level dictionary.

This book, a sequel to *Split Decisions and Other Word Puzzles*, offers a mix of 11 different puzzle types. The biggest portion is devoted to Split Decisions, my most popular invention, which appears regularly in such newspapers and magazines as *The New York Times* and *Games*. Triad Split Decisions, a variation on the Split Decision theme, and Two by Two puzzles also have large chunks devoted to them. In between are a sprinkling of other variety word puzzles, both hard and easy. Answers are provided for all the puzzles, so if you get stuck feel free to peek for a hint—I don't want you to curse me out if you can't finish. Remember: I don't like cross words!

—George Bredehorn

DIRECTIONS

ANAGRAM LOOP

Each of the longer words in the loop is an anagram of the two shorter words feeding into it. All vowels (including all Y's) have been provided. No words are repeated in the loop.

BITS & PIECES

Each set of connected pieces is a word. Each of these numbered pieces contains one or more letters that remain constant throughout the puzzle. Solving one word will help you solve others that contain the same numbered bits and pieces.

CLUELESS CROSSWORDS

Fill in the blanks in the grid so that eight seven-letter words are formed.

FILL-IN STATION

Fill in the grid with the nine letters given on the right so that three-letter words are formed in all the directions that the arrows point.

THE FINAL WORD

Unscramble the four-letter word at the top. Transfer the letter over the numbered blank to the same numbered blanks to the left of the plus signs. Continue in this fashion until you get the final word, which completes the quote. Some words may have more than one anagram, but there's only one way to get to the correct final word.

FRAZE-IT

Fill in the two defined words in each line. Keeping the letter sequence, transfer the boxed letters to the blanks below, where the phrase will appear.

LATTICEWORK

Fill in the blanks so that the words interlock and fit the category given above the grid.

MIXAGRAMS

Each line contains a five-letter word and a four-letter word whose letters have been mixed, but the left-to-right order of the letters has not been changed. Unmix the two words on each line and write them in the spaces provided. When you're done, the answer to the clue will appear in the two marked columns.

Example: D A R I U N V E T = DRIVE + AUNT

SPLIT DECISIONS

The only clues in this puzzle are the letter pairs given in the grid. Each answer consists of a pair of words that share the letters that are to be entered in the empty squares. In the example, we've filled in the letters S, I, and D to make the words SOLID and SQUID. No proper names or hyphenated words are used. A few of the combinations may have more than one possible solution, but only one will work with all the crossings.

Example: [ ] O L [ ] [ ]   becomes   S [O L] I D
               Q U   Q U

The final Split Decision on page 73 has identical letters along the diagonals of every bubble. Due to this restriction on the construction, a couple of words may be less familiar than usual.

TRIAD SPLIT DECISIONS

This puzzle is just like Split Decisions, except that three letters are given for each word instead of two. In the example, we've filled in the letters C, A, and L to make the words CEREAL and CASUAL.

Example: [ ] E R E [ ] [ ]   becomes   C [E R E] A L
               A S U   A S U

TWO BY TWO

Only two different letters are needed to complete each of these miniature crisscross puzzles. All the vowels have been placed for you. Pick two consonants and repeat them as often as necessary to finish each grid. No words are repeated in any one puzzle, and no proper names, hyphenated words, or words containing apostrophes are used.

The final Two by Two (page 68) has two sets of identical grids. The top and bottom puzzles require different letters.

SPLIT DECISIONS

Directions, page 7

Answer, page 83

TWO BY TWO

Directions, page 8

Answer, page 92

TRIAD SPLIT DECISIONS

Directions, page 7

Answer, page 75

SPLIT DECISIONS

Directions, page 7   *Answer, page 91*

MIXAGRAMS

Directions, page 7

Answer, page 90

1 | Clue: Stool pigeon, perhaps

↓   ↓

D E S H B U S H T = _ _ _ _ _ + _ _ _ _

S E D C R I T O D = _ _ _ _ _ + _ _ _ _

A G O M R E N E D = _ _ _ _ _ + _ _ _ _

U S E N A D G E S = _ _ _ _ _ + _ _ _ _

2 | Clue: Fifty cents

↓   ↓

F L O O B I E S T = _ _ _ _ _ + _ _ _ _

O C U L T I P E R = _ _ _ _ _ + _ _ _ _

C U R G O T E S S = _ _ _ _ _ + _ _ _ _

C O R E S C U R T = _ _ _ _ _ + _ _ _ _

FRAZE-IT

Directions, page 6   *Answer, page 92*

1   ☐ _ _ _☐ _☐   _☐ _☐
Church part   Chore

2   ☐ _ _☐ _☐   _☐ _☐ _
Ensemble   Main

3   ☐☐_ _ _☐ _   ☐ _☐ _
Merit   Inactive

Phrase: ‾ ‾ ‾ ‾ ‾   ‾ ‾   ‾ ‾ ‾   ‾ ‾ ‾ ‾ ‾
         1 1 1 1 1   2 2   2 2 2   3 3 3 3 3

1   ☐ _☐☐ _   ☐ _☐ _☐
Under   Halloween hag

2   _☐ _ _ _☐   _☐ _☐ _
Niece's brother   Shackle

3   ☐ _ _ _☐   _☐☐ _
Sugary   Ran away

Phrase: ‾ ‾ ‾ ‾   ‾ ‾ ‾   ‾ ‾ ‾ ‾ ‾ ‾ ‾
         1 1 1 1   1 1 2   2 2 2 3 3 3 3

SPLIT DECISIONS

Directions, page 7   *Answer, page 75*

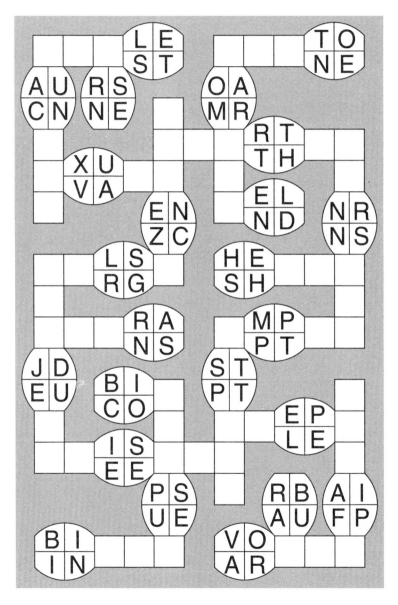

TRIAD SPLIT DECISIONS

Directions, page 7

Answer, page 77

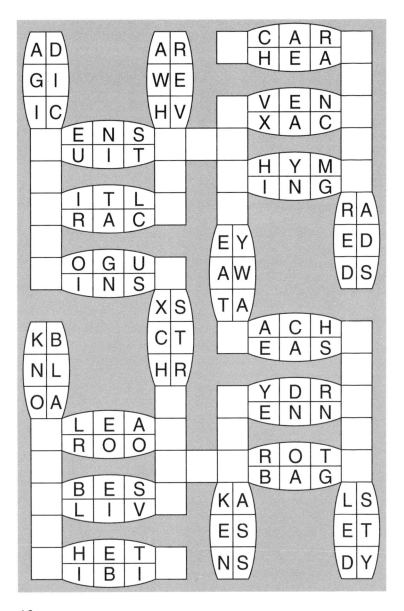

TWO BY TWO

Directions, page 8

Answer, page 90

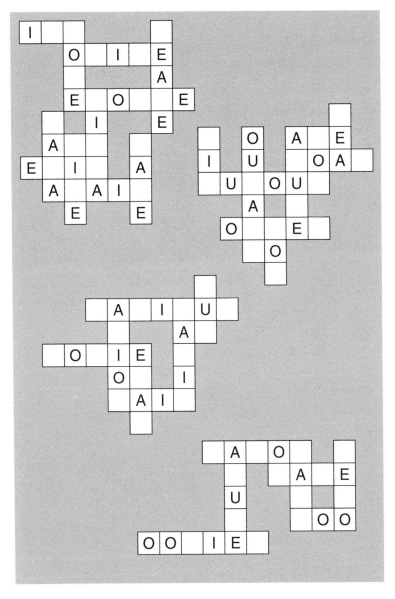

SPLIT DECISIONS

Directions, page 7

Answer, page 74

BITS & PIECES

Directions, page 6

Answer, page 88

9	7	6

Sticky stuff

8	9	7

Meal

2	6	

Hereditary unit

5	1

Sticky stuff

4	1	

Cunning

7	6	5

Precipitous

8	7	

Take five

2	8	

Type

3	5	

Ready for surgery

6	8	

Before

1	2	

Ozone element

3	1	

Authorized agent

7	5	

Pace

4	8	6	7

Most liberated

8	6	4

Ridge of rocks

9	8	

Peel

THE FINAL WORD

Directions, page 6   *Answer, page 82*

1

$$\underline{U}\ \underline{T}\ \underline{O}\ \underline{H} = \_\ \_\ \_\ \underline{\_}_1$$

$$\underline{\_}_1 + \underline{D}\ \underline{E}\ \underline{X}\ \underline{E} = \_\ \_\ \_\ \underline{\_}_2$$

$$\underline{\_}_1\ \underline{\_}_2 + \underline{N}\ \underline{E}\ \underline{S}\ \underline{Q} = \_\ \_\ \_\ \_\ \underline{\_}_3$$

$$\underline{\_}_1\ \underline{\_}_2\ \underline{\_}_3 + \underline{B}\ \underline{I}\ \underline{R}\ \underline{R} = \_\ \_\ \_\ \_\ \_\ \underline{\_}_4$$

$$\underline{\_}_1\ \underline{\_}_2\ \underline{\_}_3\ \underline{\_}_4 + \underline{V}\ \underline{E}\ \underline{I}\ \underline{N} = \_\ \_\ \_\ \_\ \_\ \_\ \_\ \_$$

The Final Word

"To make an apple pie from scratch, you must first invent the ___."   —Carl Sagan

2

$$\underline{C}\ \underline{L}\ \underline{O}\ \underline{B} = \_\ \_\ \_\ \underline{\_}_1$$

$$\underline{\_}_1 + \underline{D}\ \underline{R}\ \underline{O}\ \underline{W} = \_\ \_\ \_\ \underline{\_}_2$$

$$\underline{\_}_1\ \underline{\_}_2 + \underline{I}\ \underline{V}\ \underline{E}\ \underline{E} = \_\ \_\ \_\ \_\ \underline{\_}_3$$

$$\underline{\_}_1\ \underline{\_}_2\ \underline{\_}_3 + \underline{E}\ \underline{V}\ \underline{I}\ \underline{E} = \_\ \_\ \_\ \_\ \_\ \underline{\_}_4$$

$$\underline{\_}_1\ \underline{\_}_2\ \underline{\_}_3\ \underline{\_}_4 + \underline{U}\ \underline{N}\ \underline{I}\ \underline{A} = \_\ \_\ \_\ \_\ \_\ \_\ \_\ \_$$

The Final Word

"To have a large ___ is not obscene. To want one is."   —Ned Rorem

SPLIT DECISIONS

TRIAD SPLIT DECISIONS

Directions, page 7

Answer, page 85

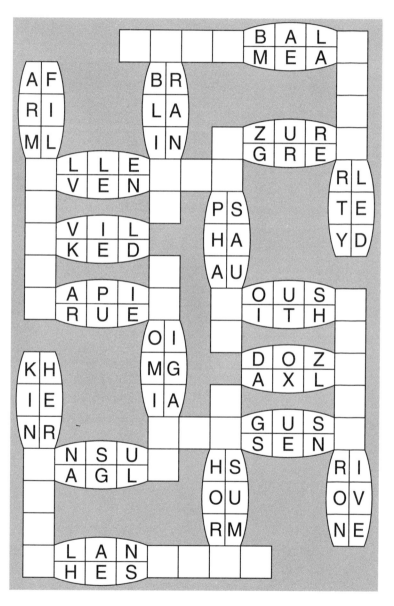

FRAZE-IT

Directions, page 6   *Answer, page 90*

1 ☐ _ ☐ _ ☐
Necklace part

☐ _ ☐ _ _ ☐ _
Jam ingredient?

2 _ ☐ _ ☐ _
Python, for example

☐ _ _ _ ☐☐
Inquiring

3 ☐ _ _ _ _ ☐
Reply

_ ☐ _ _ ☐ _
Movement

Phrase: $\overline{\underset{1}{\quad}}\,\overline{\underset{1}{\quad}}\,\overline{\underset{1}{\quad}}\,\overline{\underset{1}{\quad}}\,\overline{\underset{1}{\quad}}\,\overline{\underset{1}{\quad}}\,\overline{\underset{2}{\quad}}$ $\overline{\underset{2}{\quad}}\,\overline{\underset{2}{\quad}}\,\overline{\underset{2}{\quad}}\,\overline{\underset{2}{\quad}}\,\overline{\underset{3}{\quad}}\,\overline{\underset{3}{\quad}}\,\overline{\underset{3}{\quad}}\,\overline{\underset{3}{\quad}}$

1 ☐ _ _ _ ☐ _ ☐ _ ☐
Hawaiian fruit

☐ _ _
Scarlet

2 ☐ _ _ ☐ _
Met offering

☐ _ _ _ ☐ _
Folks

3 ☐ _ ☐ _ _ ☐
Help

_ ☐ _ ☐ _
Spiel

Phrase: $\overline{\underset{1}{\quad}}\,\overline{\underset{1}{\quad}}\,\overline{\underset{1}{\quad}}\,\overline{\underset{1}{\quad}}\,\overline{\underset{1}{\quad}}$ $\overline{\underset{2}{\quad}}\,\overline{\underset{2}{\quad}}$ $\overline{\underset{2}{\quad}}\,\overline{\underset{3}{\quad}}\,\overline{\underset{3}{\quad}}\,\overline{\underset{3}{\quad}}\,\overline{\underset{3}{\quad}}\,\overline{\underset{3}{\quad}}$

SPLIT DECISIONS

Directions, page 7

Answer, page 77

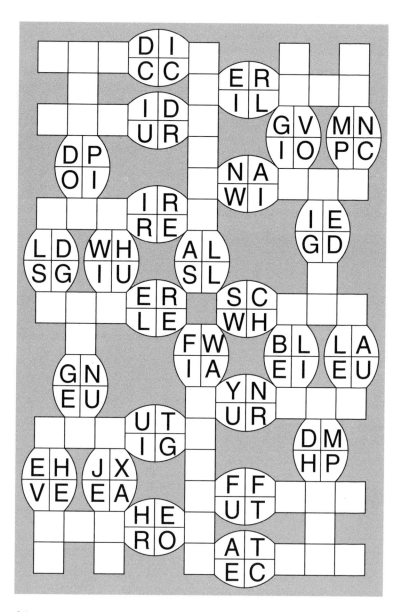

TWO BY TWO

Directions, page 8

Answer, page 80

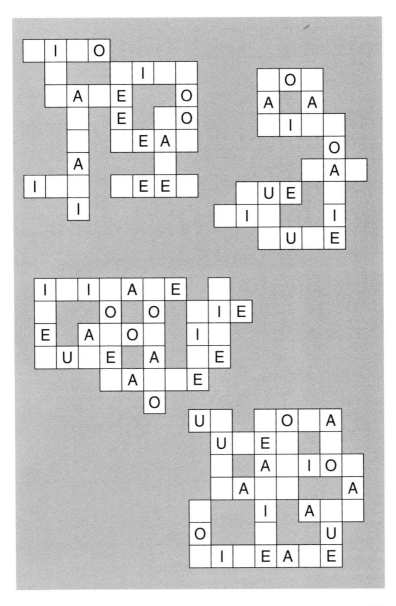

TRIAD SPLIT DECISIONS

Directions, page 7

Answer, page 83

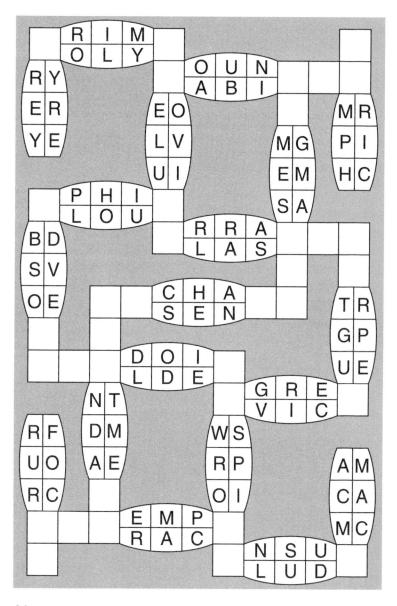

SPLIT DECISIONS

Directions, page 7

Answer, page 89

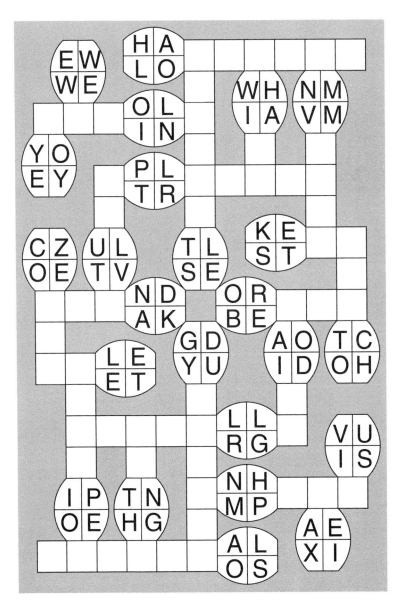

MIXAGRAMS

Directions, page 7   *Answer, page 79*

1   Clue: It's needed after the bell

↓   ↓

P A W C H O R E L = _ _ _ _ _ + _ _ _ _

A B A L L S E A S = _ _ _ _ _ + _ _ _ _

S A B L E G E A T = _ _ _ _ _ + _ _ _ _

S T E N O S E A P = _ _ _ _ _ + _ _ _ _

2   Clue: Strikes at home

↓   ↓

S I T W I F E M T = _ _ _ _ _ + _ _ _ _

A R D I N R E O W = _ _ _ _ _ + _ _ _ _

S U P H O R N U G = _ _ _ _ _ + _ _ _ _

C A S H I L I P S = _ _ _ _ _ + _ _ _ _

SPLIT DECISIONS

Directions, page 7

Answer, page 81

TRIAD SPLIT DECISIONS

Directions, page 7

Answer, page 85

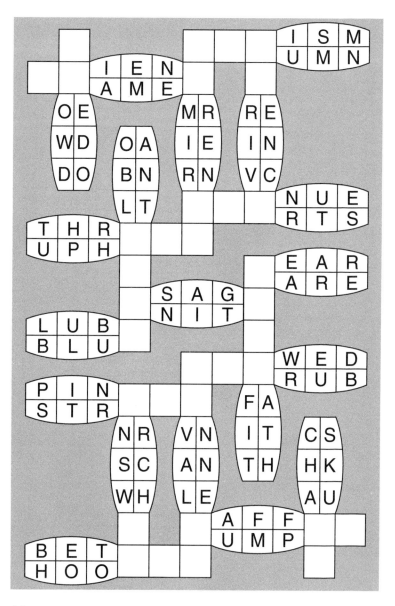

LATTICEWORK

Directions, page 7   *Answer, page 87*

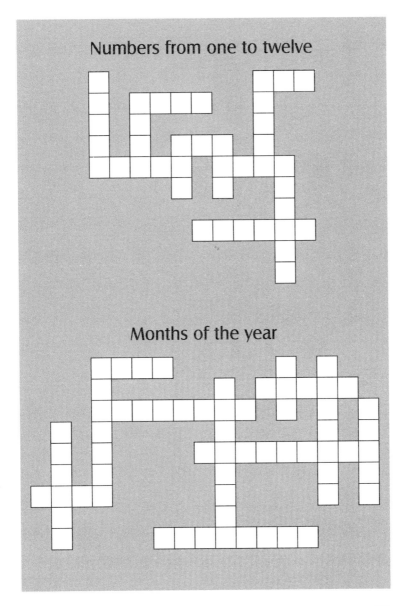

Numbers from one to twelve

Months of the year

SPLIT DECISIONS

Directions, page 7

Answer, page 75

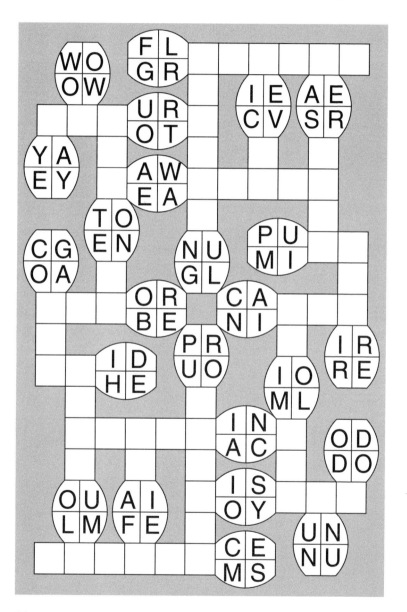

TWO BY TWO

Directions, page 8

Answer, page 78

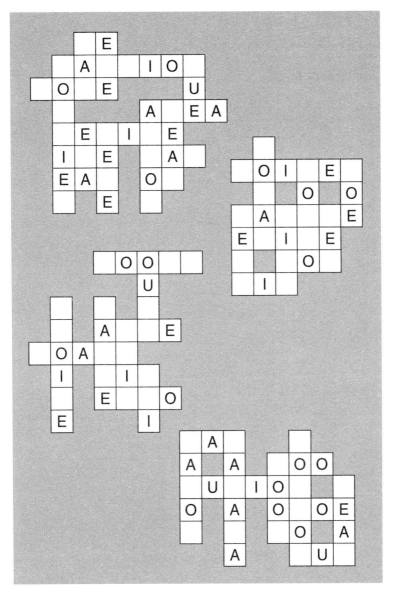

BITS & PIECES

Directions, page 6

Answer, page 82

7	3	8

Article

5	8	7	3

Strike sharply

5	2	4

Strong

1	3

Sit for an artist

6	3

Arrive

5	7	6

TV offering

1	7

Put forward as fact

6	1	3

Create

1	2	3

Bearing

4	3

Tint

6	3	4

Humorous play

6	1	7	3

Made of many parts

5	7	3

Location

1	5	3

Search party

6	8	7

Perform

8	7	3	5

Tiny arachnids

34

SPLIT DECISIONS

Directions, page 7

Answer, page 85

TRIAD SPLIT DECISIONS

Directions, page 7

Answer, page 89

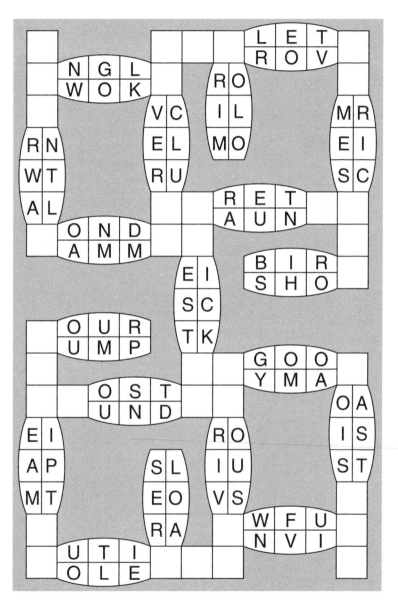

THE FINAL WORD

Directions, page 6   *Answer, page 84*

1

W I I K = _ _ _ $\overline{1}$

$\overline{1}$ + T O I D = _ _ _ _ $\overline{2}$

$\overline{1}\ \overline{2}$ + S E A F = _ _ _ _ _ $\overline{3}$

$\overline{1}\ \overline{2}\ \overline{3}$ + S K E M = _ _ _ _ _ _ $\overline{4}$

$\overline{1}\ \overline{2}\ \overline{3}\ \overline{4}$ + T E S H = _ _ _ _ _ _ _ _

The Final Word

"If a writer has to rob his mother, he will not ___: The 'Ode on a Grecian Urn' is worth any number of old ladies."

—William Faulkner

2

B U R C = _ _ _ $\overline{1}$

$\overline{1}$ + A N I C = _ _ _ _ $\overline{2}$

$\overline{1}\ \overline{2}$ + A L I O = _ _ _ _ _ $\overline{3}$

$\overline{1}\ \overline{2}\ \overline{3}$ + B O S H = _ _ _ _ _ _ $\overline{4}$

$\overline{1}\ \overline{2}\ \overline{3}\ \overline{4}$ + S M I B = _ _ _ _ _ _ _ _

The Final Word

"Arrogance and ___ live in adjoining rooms and use common currency."

—Morely Safer

SPLIT DECISIONS

Directions, page 7

Answer, page 81

MIXAGRAMS

Directions, page 7   *Answer, page 93*

1 | Clue: Music or marble

↓   ↓

E T R I C H I C E = _ _ _ _ _ + _ _ _ _

C R O N A T O N E = _ _ _ _ _ + _ _ _ _

T O R C H S O W O = _ _ _ _ _ + _ _ _ _

R A K D A R I N G = _ _ _ _ _ + _ _ _ _

2 | Clue: Where you may turn to port

↓   ↓

S L O W H E R O D = _ _ _ _ _ + _ _ _ _

H A L O I G O N D = _ _ _ _ _ + _ _ _ _

F O G E N C R E E = _ _ _ _ _ + _ _ _ _

A P I D E P E R T = _ _ _ _ _ + _ _ _ _

TWO BY TWO

Directions, page 8   *Answer, page 84*

SPLIT DECISIONS

Directions, page 7

Answer, page 89

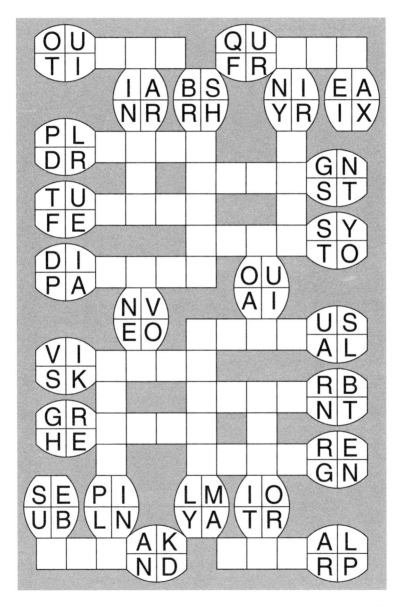

TRIAD SPLIT DECISIONS

Directions, page 7

Answer, page 77

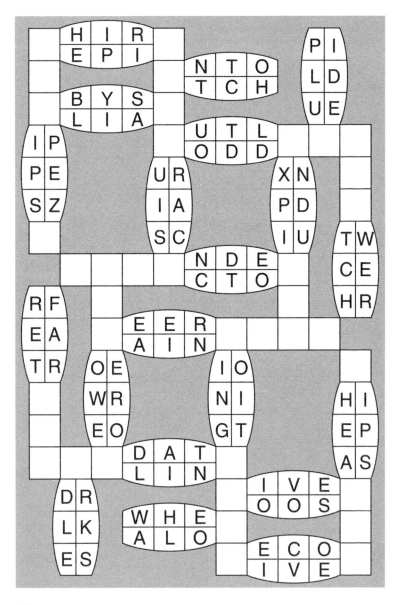

LATTICEWORK

Directions, page 7 *Answer, page 79*

Colors of the spectrum

Planets in our solar system

SPLIT DECISIONS

Directions, page 7   *Answer, page 74*

FILL-IN STATION

Directions, page 6   *Answer, page 86*

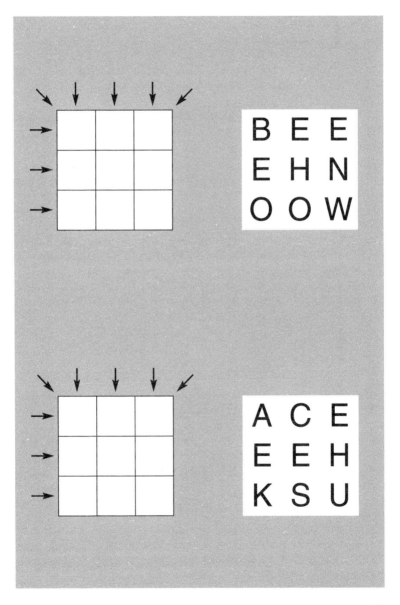

TWO BY TWO

Directions, page 8

Answer, page 82

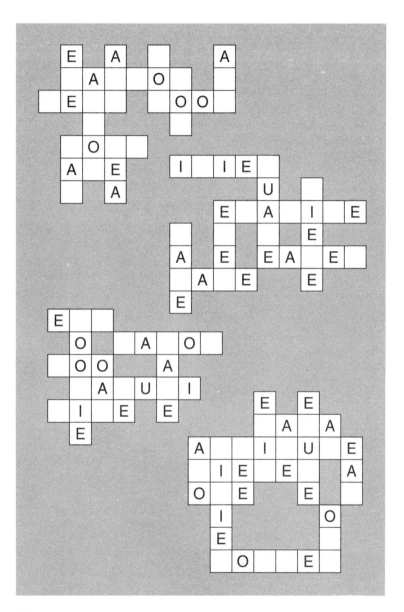

SPLIT DECISIONS

Directions, page 7

Answer, page 77

TRIAD SPLIT DECISIONS

Directions, page 7

Answer, page 91

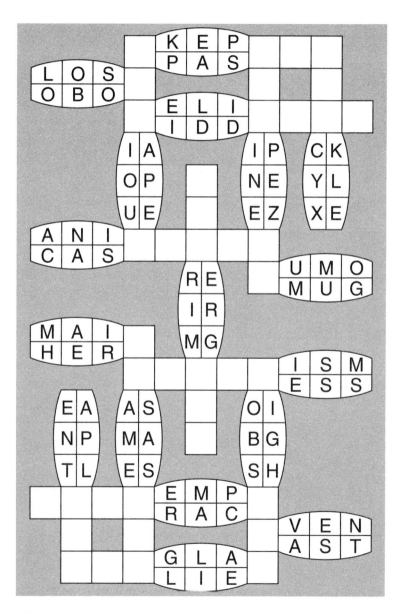

CLUELESS CROSSWORDS

Directions, page 6

Answer, page 78

SPLIT DECISIONS

Directions, page 7 *Answer, page 79*

MIXAGRAMS

Directions, page 7   *Answer, page 84*

1

Clue: Training regimen

ANTERWACK = _ _ _ _ _ + _ _ _ _

CHEOUROPE = _ _ _ _ _ + _ _ _ _

LAPPOSORE = _ _ _ _ _ + _ _ _ _

PADEDLEAK = _ _ _ _ _ + _ _ _ _

2

Clue: Kind of cake

GASPUZOTE = _ _ _ _ _ + _ _ _ _

BOVERALET = _ _ _ _ _ + _ _ _ _

BRABUSETH = _ _ _ _ _ + _ _ _ _

PUPTOOTLY = _ _ _ _ _ + _ _ _ _

TWO BY TWO

Directions, page 8

Answer, page 86

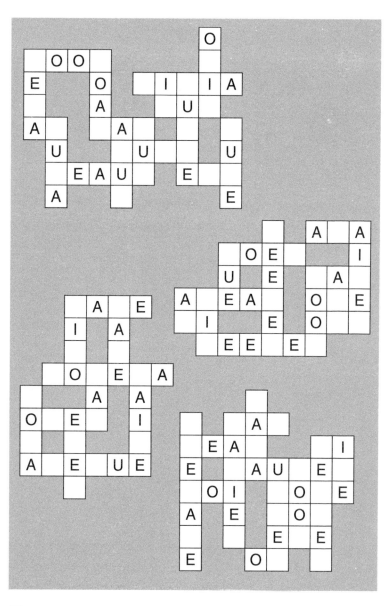

SPLIT DECISIONS

Directions, page 7

Answer, page 81

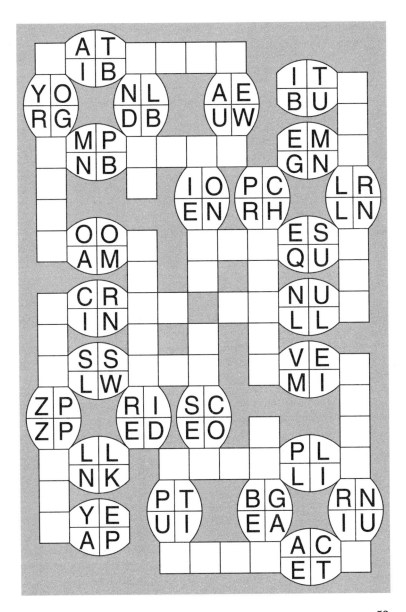

ANAGRAM LOOP

Directions, page 6

Answer, page 88

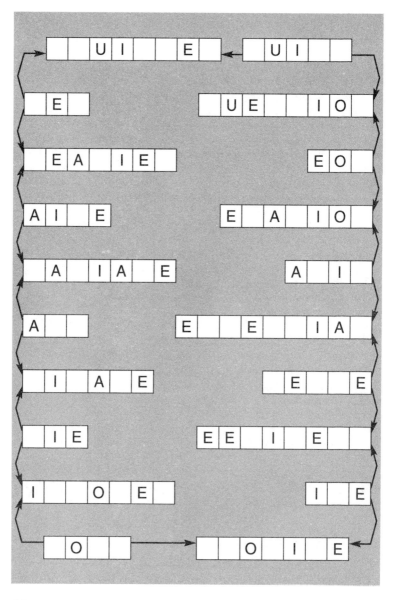

SPLIT DECISIONS

Directions, page 7

Answer, page 83

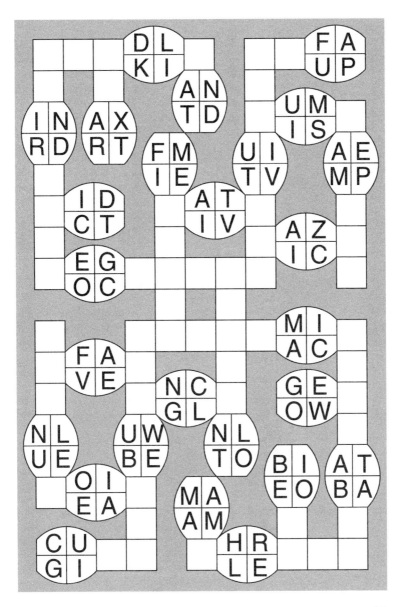

TRIAD SPLIT DECISIONS

Directions, page 7

Answer, page 74

THE FINAL WORD

Directions, page 6   *Answer, page 88*

1

$$\underline{S} \ A \ X \ \underline{I} = \_ \ \_ \ \_ \ \underset{1}{\_}$$

$$\underset{1}{\_} + \underline{R} \ \underline{I} \ \underline{T} \ \underline{H} = \_ \ \_ \ \_ \ \underset{2}{\_}$$

$$\underset{1}{\_} \ \underset{2}{\_} + \underline{T} \ E \ E \ \underline{L} = \_ \ \_ \ \_ \ \_ \ \underset{3}{\_}$$

$$\underset{1}{\_} \ \underset{2}{\_} \ \underset{3}{\_} + \underline{Y} \ \underline{E} \ L \ \underline{N} = \_ \ \_ \ \_ \ \_ \ \_ \ \underset{4}{\_}$$

$$\underset{1}{\_} \ \underset{2}{\_} \ \underset{3}{\_} \ \underset{4}{\_} + \underline{R} \ \underline{I} \ \underline{V} \ \underline{E} = \_ \ \_ \ \_ \ \_ \ \_ \ \_ \ \_ \ \_$$

The Final Word

"Summer has set in with its usual ___." —Samuel Coleridge

2

$$\underline{U} \ \underline{R} \ \underline{O} \ \underline{P} = \_ \ \_ \ \_ \ \underset{1}{\_}$$

$$\underset{1}{\_} + \underline{D} \ O \ \underline{P} \ \underline{O} = \_ \ \_ \ \_ \ \underset{2}{\_}$$

$$\underset{1}{\_} \ \underset{2}{\_} + \underline{O} \ \underline{N} \ \underline{D} \ \underline{A} = \_ \ \_ \ \_ \ \_ \ \underset{3}{\_}$$

$$\underset{1}{\_} \ \underset{2}{\_} \ \underset{3}{\_} + \underline{E} \ \underline{C} \ \underline{I} \ \underline{O} = \_ \ \_ \ \_ \ \_ \ \_ \ \underset{4}{\_}$$

$$\underset{1}{\_} \ \underset{2}{\_} \ \underset{3}{\_} \ \underset{4}{\_} + \underline{A} \ \underline{B} \ \underline{U} \ \underline{M} = \_ \ \_ \ \_ \ \_ \ \_ \ \_ \ \_ \ \_$$

The Final Word

"A ___ of somber dignity has descended over his reputation."   —James Atlas

SPLIT DECISIONS

Directions, page 7

Answer, page 85

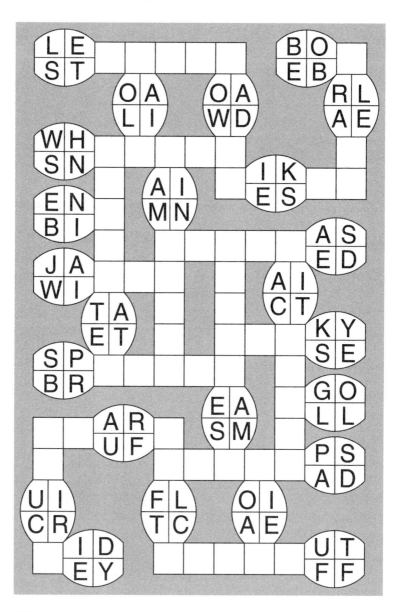

TWO BY TWO

Directions, page 8

Answer, page 88

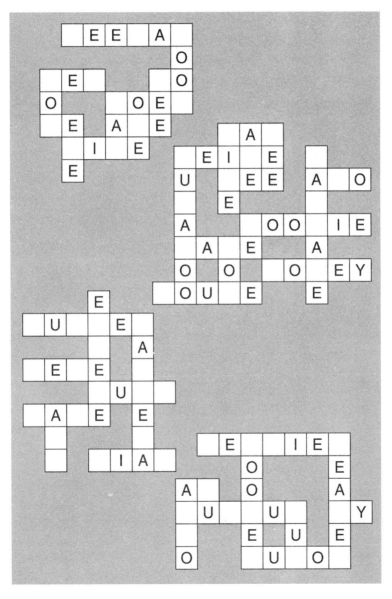

LATTICEWORK

Directions, page 7　　　　　　　　　　　　*Answer, page 93*

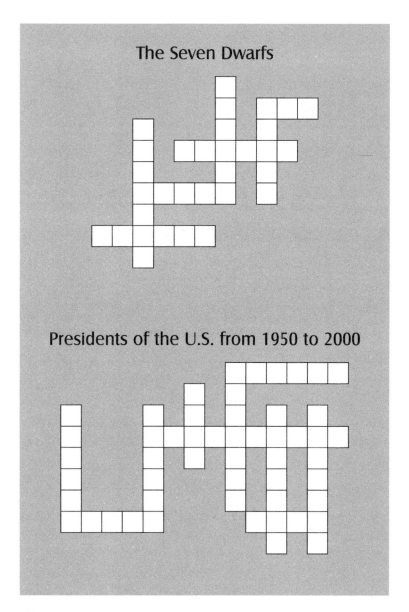

The Seven Dwarfs

Presidents of the U.S. from 1950 to 2000

SPLIT DECISIONS

Directions, page 7

Answer, page 81

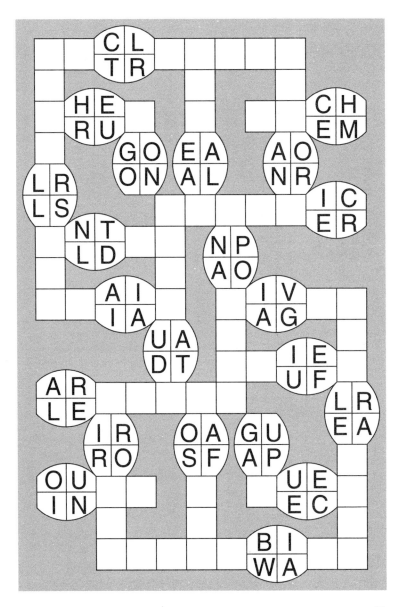

TRIAD SPLIT DECISIONS

Directions, page 7

Answer, page 83

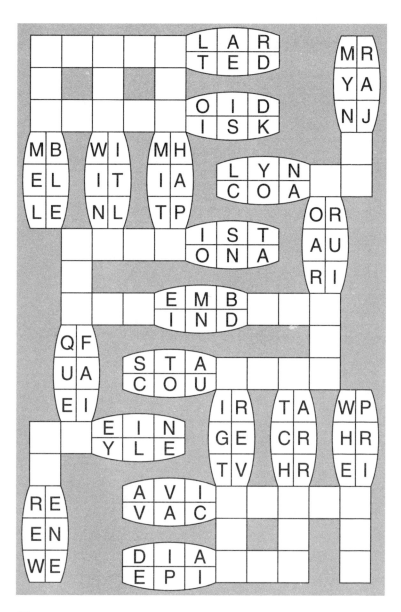

MIXAGRAMS

Directions, page 7   *Answer, page 87*

1 | Clue: Turkey choice

TCLOHUDEM = _ _ _ _ _ + _ _ _ _

KAMPIPATE = _ _ _ _ _ + _ _ _ _

ARALTIARA = _ _ _ _ _ + _ _ _ _

SABUPTOOK = _ _ _ _ _ + _ _ _ _

2 | Clue: Hoop coup

SLEADANDY = _ _ _ _ _ + _ _ _ _

LISOLACUP = _ _ _ _ _ + _ _ _ _

SALYINACS = _ _ _ _ _ + _ _ _ _

MOBGIKULE = _ _ _ _ _ + _ _ _ _

SPLIT DECISIONS

Directions, page 7

Answer, page 74

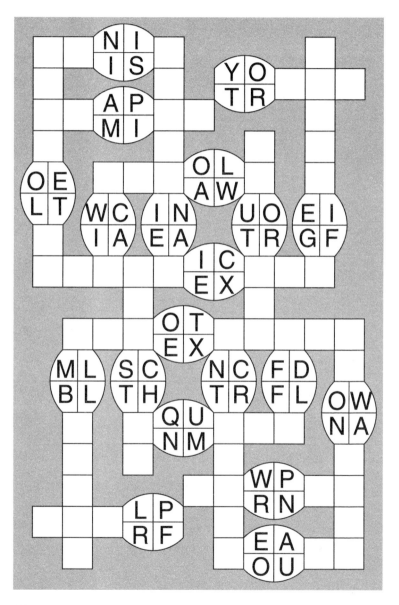

FILL-IN STATION

Directions, page 6

Answer, page 80

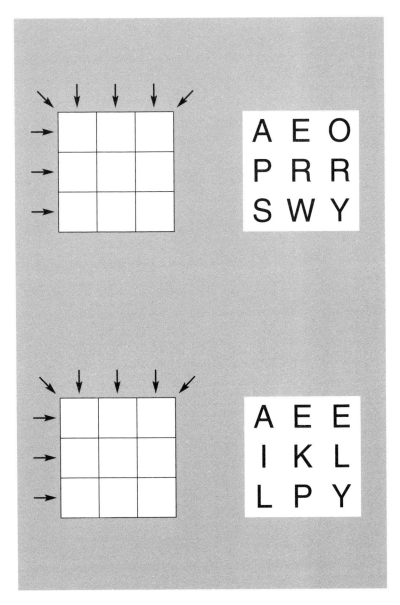

TRIAD SPLIT DECISIONS

Directions, page 7

Answer, page 91

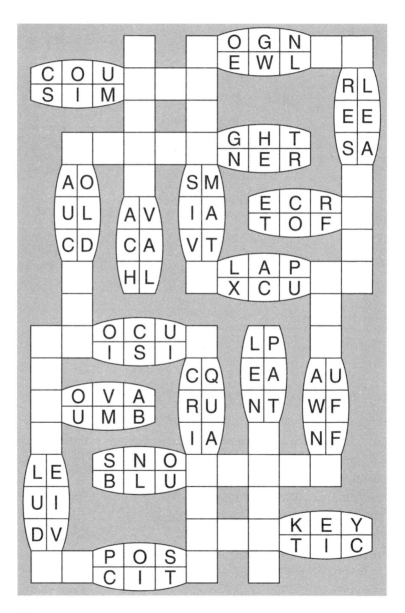

SPLIT DECISIONS

Directions, page 7

Answer, page 89

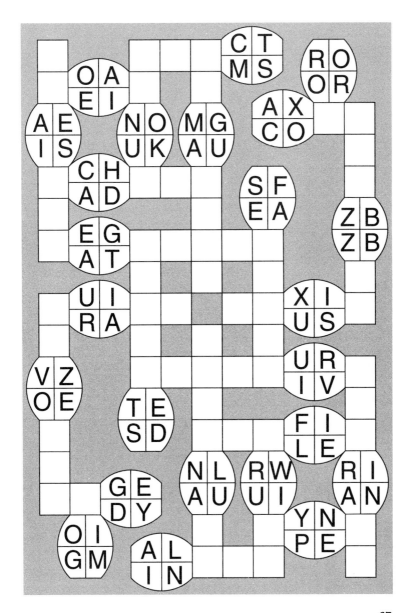

TWO BY TWO

Directions, page 8   *Answer, page 76*

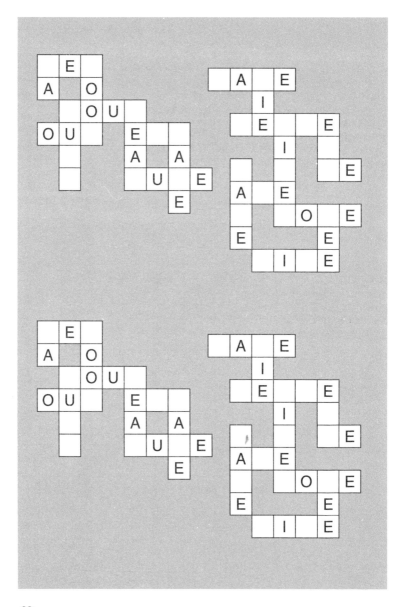

CLUELESS CROSSWORDS

Directions, page 6

Puzzle 1 (7×7 grid):

	K		M			
T	■	G	■	L	■	
		N	U			S
M	■		■	Q	■	
			F			
	■	U	■		■	L
D					T	

Puzzle 2 (7×6 grid):

B		Q				
	■		■		■	
	M				U	
	■		■		■	K
N		T			T	
	■		■	L	■	Y
		R		D	L	

SPLIT DECISIONS

Directions, page 7

Answer, page 91

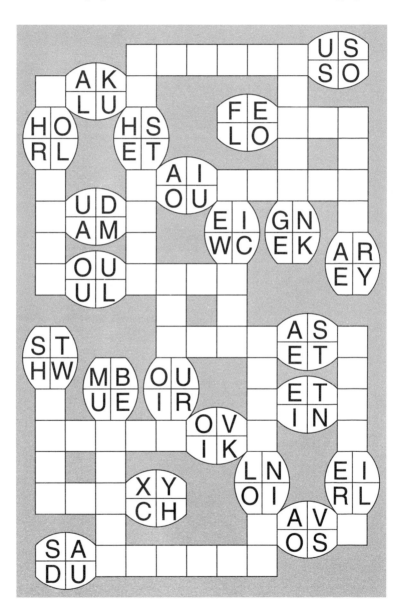

TRIAD SPLIT DECISIONS

Directions, page 7   *Answer, page 75*

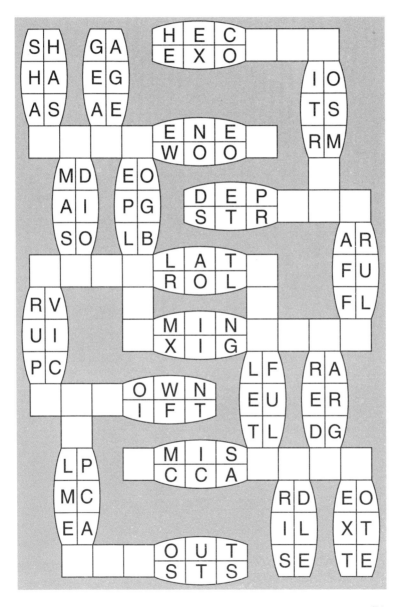

ANAGRAM LOOP

Directions, page 6

Answer, page 80

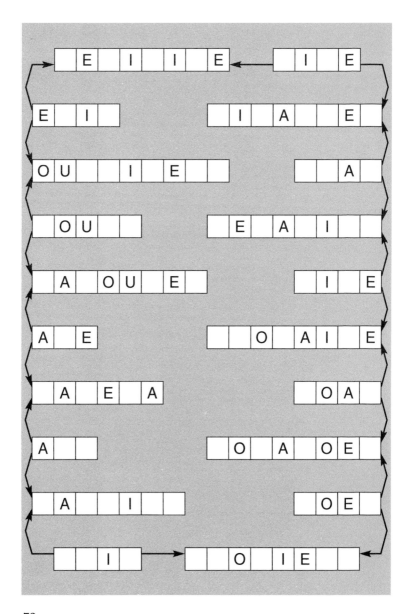

SPLIT DECISIONS

Directions, page 7

Answer, page 93

18 SPLIT DECISIONS

44 SPLIT DECISIONS

64 SPLIT DECISIONS

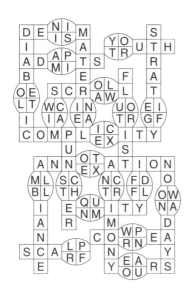

56 TRIAD SPLIT

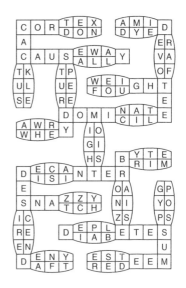

15 SPLIT DECISIONS

32 SPLIT DECISIONS

71 TRIAD SPLIT

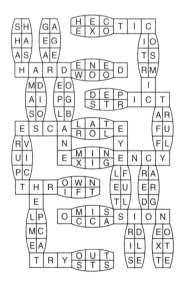

11 TRIAD SPLIT

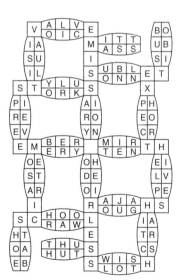

68 TWO BY TWO

```
L E T           B A L E
A   O               I
  L O U T       B E L L E
O U T   E L L       I   B
  L     A   A   B   B   B E
  L     L U T E A L E
        E       B   L O B E
                E       E
                  B I L E

P E P           R A V E
A   O               I
  P O U R       V E R V E
O U R   E R R       I   R
  R     A   A   R   V   R E
  R     P U R E A R E
        E       R   R O V E
                E       E
                  R I V E
```

69 CLUELESS CROSSWORDS

S	K	I	M	P	E	D
T	■	G	■	L	■	I
A	N	N	U	A	L	S
M	■	E	■	Q	■	P
P	R	O	F	U	S	E
E	■	U	■	E	■	L
D	E	S	I	S	T	S

B	E	Q	U	E	S	T
R	■	U	■	M	■	U
A	M	A	T	E	U	R
I	■	R	■	R	■	K
N	I	T	R	A	T	E
E	■	E	■	L	■	Y
D	I	R	N	D	L	S

76

24 SPLIT DECISIONS

47 SPLIT DECISIONS

42 TRIAD SPLIT

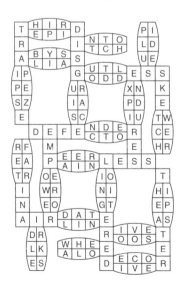

16 TRIAD SPLIT

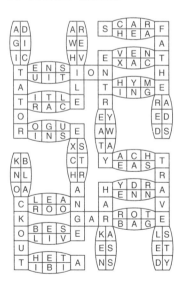

33 TWO BY TWO

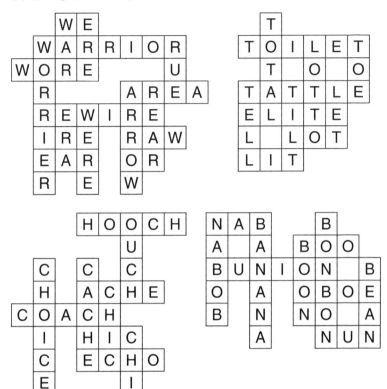

49 CLUELESS CROSSWORDS

R	E	V	I	V	A	L
E		A		I		I
P	I	C	C	O	L	O
A		C		L		N
I	M	I	T	A	T	E
R		N		T		S
S	H	E	K	E	L	S

P	A	J	A	M	A	S
R		E		O		L
E	X	A	M	I	N	E
F		L		S		D
A	B	O	R	T	E	D
C		U		E		E
E	N	S	U	R	E	D

28 MIXAGRAMS

WHORL + PACE
BALSA + ALES
BLEAT + SAGE
TENSE + SOAP
LATE PASS

SWIFT + ITEM
ARROW + DINE
SHRUG + UPON
CHILI + ASPS
FOUL TIPS

50 SPLIT DECISIONS

43 LATTICEWORK

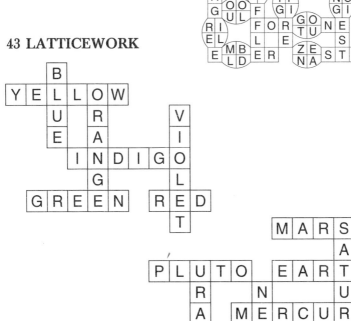

25 TWO BY TWO

65 FILL-IN STATION

72 ANAGRAM LOOP
Clockwise from top left: DEFINITE, FINE, FINAGLED, GLAD, PEDALING, PINE, PTOMAINE, MOAT, TOMATOES, TOES, STONIEST, SNIT, MARTINS, ARM, CAMERA, ACE, CAROUSES, SOURS, OUTSIDERS, EDIT

29 SPLIT DECISIONS

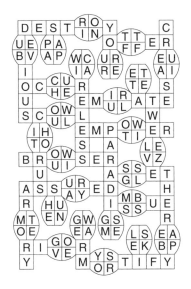

53 SPLIT DECISIONS

38 SPLIT DECISIONS

61 SPLIT DECISIONS

46 TWO BY TWO

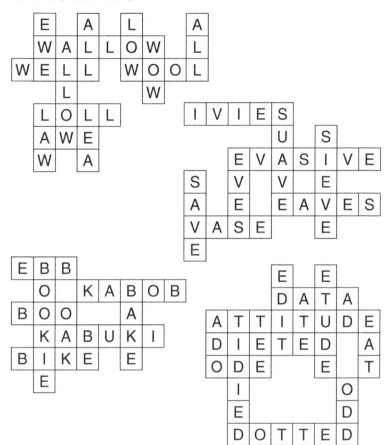

34 BITS & PIECES
Reading down: ITEM, STURDY, COME, POSIT,
POSTURE, COMEDY, SITE, COMMIT, SMITE, POSE,
SITCOM, COMPOSE, DYE, COMPOSITE, POSSE,
MITES

20 THE FINAL WORD
1 THOU, EXUDE, QUEENS, BRUISER, UNIVERSE
2 BLOC, CROWD, DEVICE, DECEIVE, AUDIENCE

9 SPLIT DECISIONS

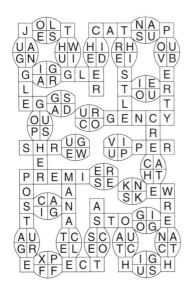

55 SPLIT DECISIONS

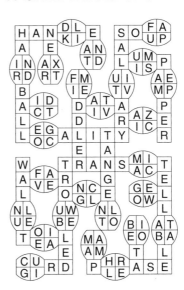

26 TRIAD SPLIT

62 TRIAD SPLIT

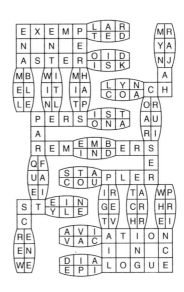

40 TWO BY TWO

```
C A R I O C A      U         S
A   O   C          S T A S I S
R O C O C O        E S T A T E
R       U          S E T T E E
I C I E R            T E E S
E       C          A S S
C R I E R          S E T
        U
```

```
M E D I U M        H U L A       H
U   U     I        U     L   H E
D U M D U M        L     O H   E
D   M     E        L     H E L L
I D I O M            H E A L
E   E   U            A     L
D   D I M E      H A I L   H O L E
                     E
```

51 MIXAGRAMS

TRACK + ANEW   GAUZE + SPOT
COUPE + HERO   BERET + OVAL
LAPSE + POOR   BRUSH + ABET
ADDLE + PEAK   PUTTY + POOL
ROAD WORK   ZEST SOAP

37 THE FINAL WORD

1 KIWI, IDIOT, FIESTA, MISTAKE, HESITATE
2 CURB, CABIN, ALBINO, HOBNOBS, SNOBBISM

35 SPLIT DECISIONS

58 SPLIT DECISIONS

22 TRIAD SPLIT

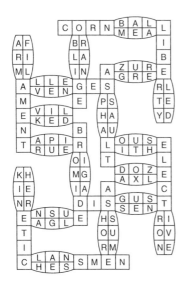

30 TRIAD SPLIT

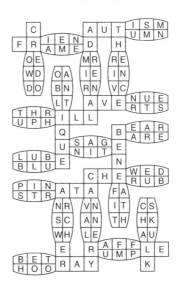

52 TWO BY TWO

```
                O
B  O  O  B      B     T  I  B  I  A
E        O            T  U  T
T        A            T        T
A  T     T  A  B      T              T
   U        B  U  T   T              U
   B  E  A  U  T      E  B  B        E
   A        T                       E
```

```
      V  A  N  E
      I        A
      N        A
   N  O  V  E  N  A
N        A        A
O  V  E  N        I
V        V        V
A  V  E  N  U  E
         N
```

```
               H        A  H  A
            H  O  E  D         I
               U     E     H  A  D
   A  H  E  A  D        O  D  E
   H  I        E        O  D  D
      D  E  E  D  E  D
```

```
            P
P        R  A  P
R  E  A  P              P  I
E        P  A  U  P  E  R
P  O  I        P  O  P  E
A        E     P  O  P
R        R     E  R  E
E           O  R        R
```

45 FILL-IN STATION

```
W  E  B        S  A  C
H  O  E        H  U  E
O  N  E        E  K  E
```

86

31 LATTICEWORK

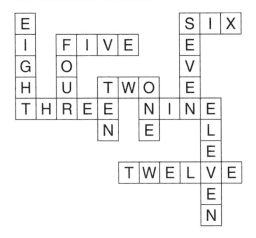

63 MIXAGRAMS

CLOUD + THEM   SEDAN + LADY

KAPPA + MITE   LILAC + SOUP

ALTAR + ARIA   ALIAS + SYNC

SPOOK + ABUT   MOGUL + BIKE

DARK MEAT   SLAM DUNK

59 TWO BY TWO

```
S E E S A W        G A G
          W      B E I G E    B
S E W   S O      B U   B E E  A G O
S O   W O E S    G   E        G
W E   A W E      A       B O O G I E
  W I S E        B A B E      A
  E              O   O   B O G E Y
              G O U G E        E

      E
T U F F E T        M E R R I E R
    F   A            O       E
F E T E F          A M   O   A
    T U F T        M U R M U R  M Y
F A T E E          M   E   U  E
    F   T          O   R U M O R
    T F I A T
```

41 SPLIT DECISIONS

67 SPLIT DECISIONS

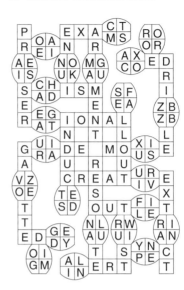

36 TRIAD SPLIT

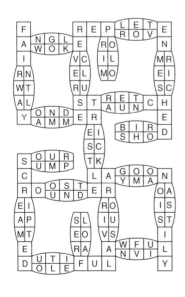

27 SPLIT DECISIONS

89

17 TWO BY TWO

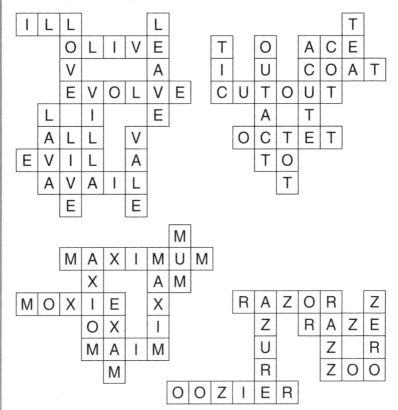

13 MIXAGRAMS

SHUSH + DEBT
SCROD + EDIT
AMEND + GORE
USAGE + ENDS
SONG BIRD

FOIST + LOBE
OUTER + CLIP
URGES + CLIP
RECUR + COST
FOUR BITS

23 FRAZE-IT

1 CLASP; TRAFFIC
2 SNAKE; ASKING
3 ANSWER; MOTION
CAPTAIN KANGAROO

1 PINEAPPLE; RED
2 OPERA; PEOPLE
3 ASSIST; PITCH
PAPER OR PLASTIC

12 SPLIT DECISIONS

70 SPLIT DECISIONS

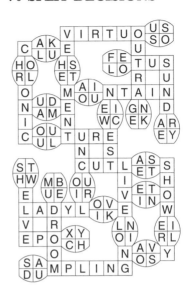

48 TRIAD SPLIT

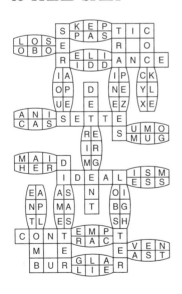

66 TRIAD SPLIT

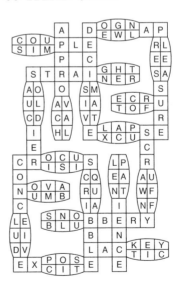

10 TWO BY TWO

21 SPLIT DECISIONS

14 FRAZE-IT
1 STEEPLE; TASK
2 OUTFIT; CHIEF
3 DESERVE; IDLE
SPEAK OF THE DEVIL

1 BELOW; WITCH
2 NEPHEW; CHAIN
3 SWEET; FLED
BLOW THE WHISTLE

39 MIXAGRAMS

ETHIC + RICE
CRANE + ONTO
TORSO + CHOW
RADAR + KING
HARD ROCK

LOWER + SHOD
ALIGN + HOOD
FENCE + OGRE
ADEPT + PIER
WINE SHOP

73 SPLIT DECISIONS

60 LATTICEWORK

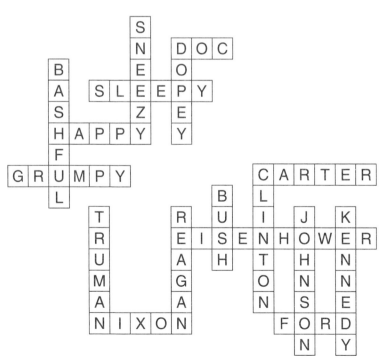

INDEX

ABOUT THE AUTHOR

GEORGE BREDEHORN is a retired teacher who lives in Wantagh, New York. Every Tuesday he and his wife Dorothy entertain a group of Long Island wordsmiths, including friends from Mensa, who play one or two of the 80-plus word games he has invented.

WHAT IS AMERICAN MENSA?

American Mensa
The High IQ Society
One out of 50 people qualifies
for American Mensa ...
Are YOU the One?

American Mensa, Ltd. is an organization for individuals who have one common trait: a score in the top two percent of the population on a standardized intelligence test. Over five million Americans are eligible for membership ... you may be one of them.

• Looking for intellectual stimulation?
You'll find a good "mental workout" in the *Mensa Bulletin,* our national magazine. Voice your opinion in the newsletter published by your local group. And attend activities and gatherings with fascinating programs and engaging conversation.

• Looking for social interaction?
There's something happening on the Mensa calendar almost daily. These range from lectures to game nights to parties. Each year, there are over 40 regional gatherings and the Annual Gathering, where you can meet people, exchange ideas, and make interesting new friends.

• Looking for others who share your special interest?
Whether your interest might be in computer gaming, Monty Python, or scuba, there's probably a Mensa Special Interest

Group (SIG) for you. There are over 150 SIGs, which are started and maintained by members.

So contact us today to receive a free brochure and application.

American Mensa, Ltd.
1229 Corporate Drive West
Arlington, TX 76006
(800) 66-MENSA
AmericanMensa@mensa.org
www.us.mensa.org

If you don't live in the U.S. and would like to get in touch with your national Mensa, contact:

Mensa International
15 The Ivories
6-8 Northampton Street, Islington
London N1 2HY England